MY BIG GOLDEN
COUNTING BOOK

By

LILIAN MOORE

With Pictures by

GARTH WILLIAMS

GOLDEN PRESS · NEW YORK

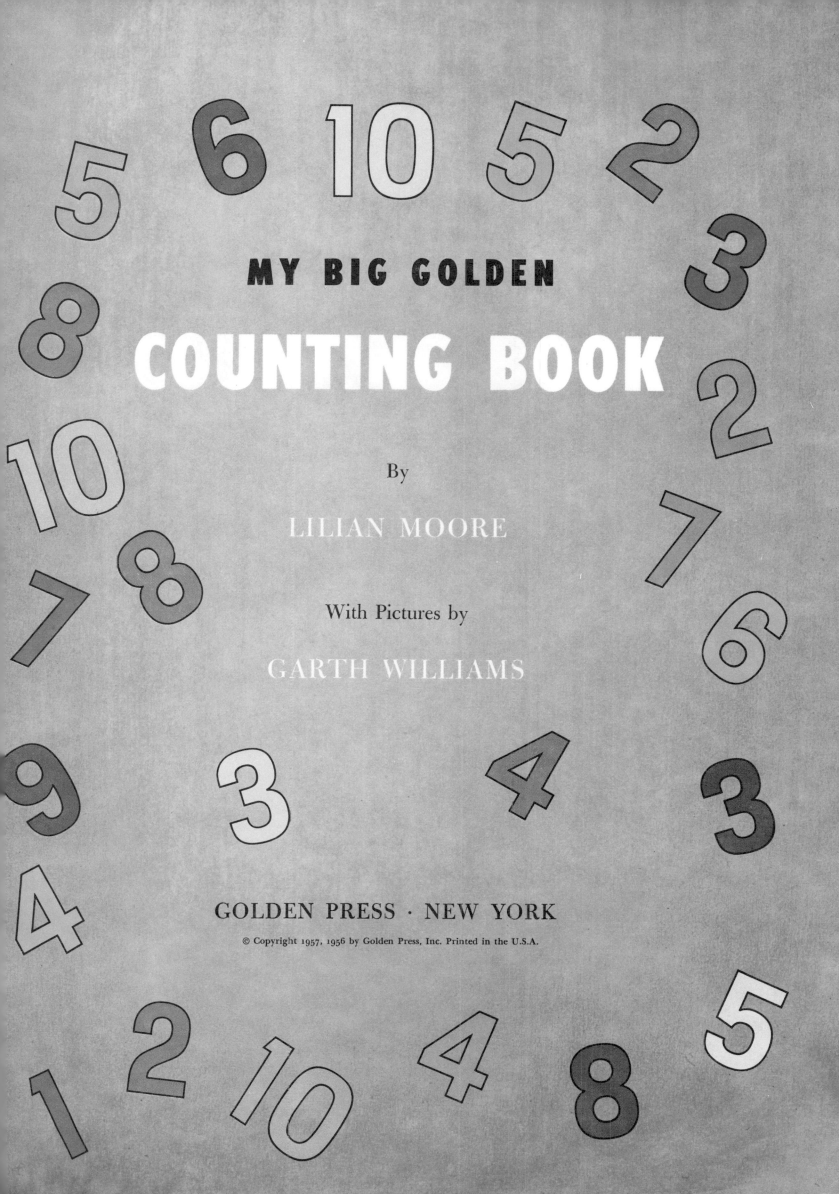

1

One little puppy,
A roly-poly puppy, alone as he can be.
"Isn't there a boy or girl
Who wants to play with me?"

Two little woolly lambs
Looking for their mother.
Two little woolly lambs,
A sister and a brother.

2

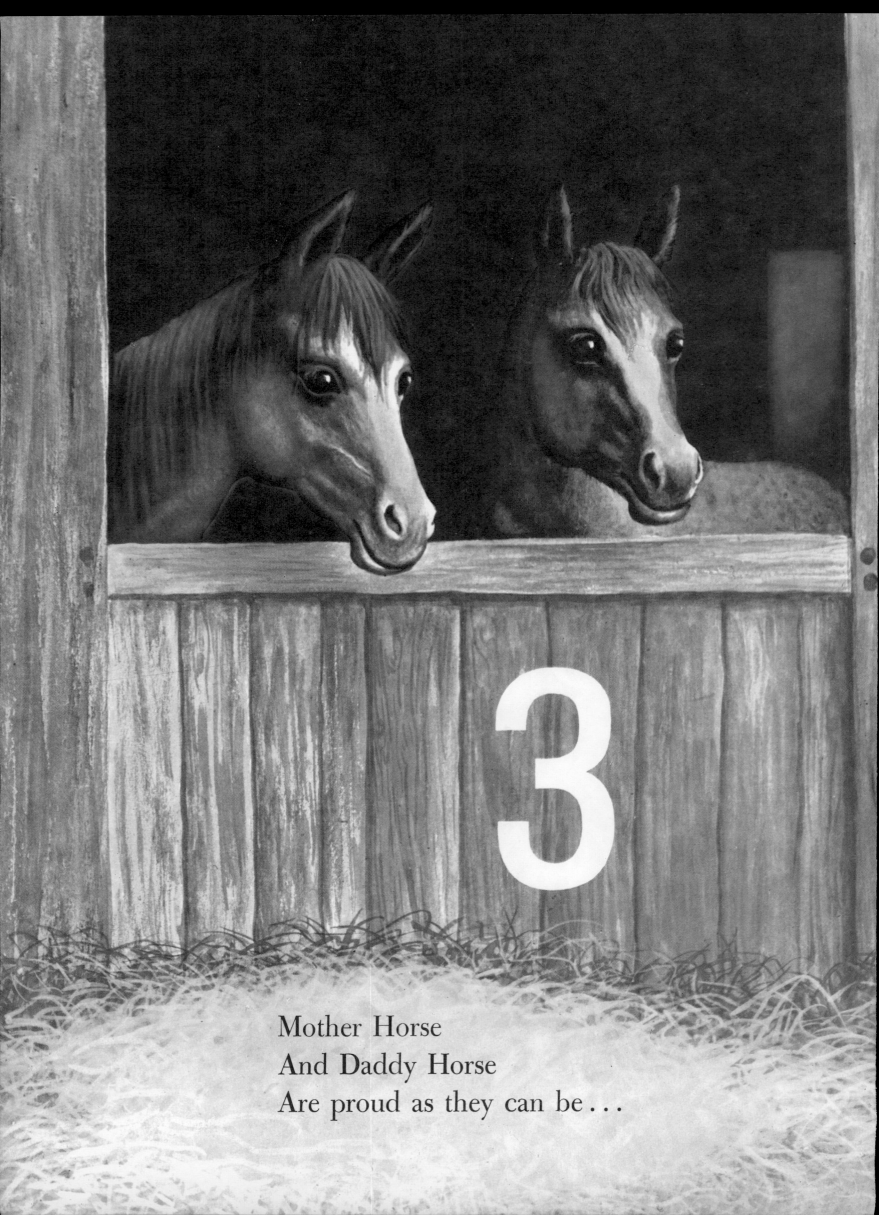

Mother Horse
And Daddy Horse
Are proud as they can be...

Because they have a baby horse
And baby horse makes three.

Four furry, purry kittens
Look alike because

Each furry, purry kitten
Has four white paws.

5

Bunny finds five cabbages
Near the garden wall.
Bunny sniffs five cabbages,
And Bunny wants them all—
One, two, three, four, five.

One, two, three,
Four, five, six.
First they were eggs...

Now, they are chicks!

Waddle, waddle, waddle,
The baby ducklings go,
Waddling after Mother Duck,
Seven in a row.

Swish, swish,
Eight fish
Swimming in the brook...

8

Swish, swish,
Wise fish,
Swimming past the hook.

High in the sky
In the shape of a "V"
How many wild geese
Can you see?

Hurry and count them
As they fly.
You will see nine geese,
And so will I!

How many nuts did you find,
Little Squirrel,
Looking high and low?
Chitter, chatter,
What's the matter?
Don't you know?
Little Squirrel, I'll tell you, then.
Little Squirrel, you found ten.

10

Five butterflies at rest.
Five butterflies at play.

Here comes kitty.
What a pity.
Now all ten fly away.

They don't waddle, they don't fly—
Which ones can they be?
Can you find them, can you count them—
There are only three.

They do not bark, they don't say peep—
Which ones can they be?
Can you find them, can you count them—
There are only four to see.

1 ONE

2 TWO

3 THREE

4 FOUR

5 FIVE

6 SIX

7 SEVEN

8 EIGHT

9 NINE

10 TEN